beautifully different

Autism : viewing the world through a different lens

MAKIKO

Matador
Unit 9 Priory Business Park
Kibworth Beauchamp
Leicester LE8 0RX, UK
Tel: (+44) 116 279 2299
Fax: (+44) 116 279 2277
Email: books@troubador.co.uk
Web: www.troubador.co.uk/matador

ISBN 978 1783063 895

British Library Cataloguing in Publication Data.
A catalogue record for this book is available from the British Library.

Typeset by Troubador Publishing Ltd, Leicester, UK

Matador is an imprint of Troubador Publishing Ltd

This is a book for parents who provide tireless efforts for their children who experienced difficult early years.

This is a book for their children whose 'uniqueness' will be their strength for the future.

MAKIKO

beautifully
different

introduction

This book was conceived for a very important reason: to help the world see children in a new light. Each child is magnificent in his or her own unique way. Each one brings a great gift into this world. Each one is so much more than anyone can ever imagine. Each is worthy of honour and the deepest, sweetest love. On occasion, certain children surprise us with unconventional qualities. They seem very different from other children. They don't relate to others in expected ways or show interest in the usual things. They may have extreme reactions to common experiences such as wearing shoes or eating certain types of food or having a change in routine. These differences cause their parents to wonder if something is wrong. In some cases, these unconventional qualities and differences, especially when accompanied by delays in acquiring important early developmental milestones, are a sign that the brain is developing in an unconventional way. In this book, you will meet some children whose unconventional developmental features reflect a different pattern of neurodevelopment known as autism spectrum disorder (ASD). These children walk a different path through life. Through this book, you have the opportunity to peer at the world through their eyes. If you contemplate each picture, each story, each child in this book, you will receive a gift. That gift will differ from reader to reader, but it is likely to enable everyone to experience more comfort with those whose perspectives are quite different from their own, to look at the world in a fresh new way, and maybe even to embrace more fully those who live on the edges of the mainstream.

What are we to think about children who are in a world apart from our own? The answer to this question begins with the brain of an infant. Babies come into the world with their own biases that evolve into their own perspectives on the world. In some cases, these perspectives are so unusual that a child may be considered odd or "too different". Take for example the child who finds great pleasure in lying on his belly, positioning his eyes at just the right angle to see the turning wheels of a toy car as he rolls it back and forth across the floor. So very different from the child who rolls the car across the floor, imagining it is speeding its way across a mountainous road. So very different from the child who is thrilled to play cars with another person, where the game of rolling the car back and forth is fun just because it provides a venue to share in an experience with someone. In this book, we focus on a group of children who see the world differently from most other children their age – we peer into the minds of children who have an ASD. Children with ASD provide the world with a generous reminder to take the time to watch, listen and understand the uniqueness of every child. If we take that time, we will learn much. Watching a child play and listening to the child express his ideas – without needing for the child to be anything other than his own precious self, will lead us to insights of great depth. These insights will lead us to know how to build a bridge from our own world into the world of the child. When such a bridge is built, we can create paths that will help the child learn, develop confidence and feel loved. We affirm the child's own unique worth. We thereby lay the foundation for a happy, healthy childhood that will translate into a healthier, happier adult. And as we go through this process, we are changed. Because the one thing that we know for certain with any child, if we watch closely enough, is that they will surprise us and teach us. Through them, we gain new insights into ways that our own perspectives or life approach could be tweaked to make us more effective in our work and interactions, and help us to bring more joy to friends, family, and co-workers.

About Autism Spectrum Disorders

Autism spectrum disorders (ASDs) occur in at least 1% of the population. About one in eighty-eight children has an ASD. More males have ASD than females, about three or four times as many. ASDs are diagnosed by professionals based on observation of a child's behaviour during specialised assessments and getting information about the child's development by interviewing caregivers. There are no medical tests or cures for ASD. Certain types of social and communication difficulties must be present, persistent and problematic in the child's day-to-day life in order for a diagnosis of ASD to be given. To qualify for a diagnosis of ASD, these difficulties must not be due to intellectual impairment, though some individuals with ASD also have intellectual disability. While we use the term ASD to refer to a group of individuals who exhibit a specific social and communication behavioural profile, no two individuals with ASD are exactly alike. As with everyone else, they have their own personality, preferences and dislikes. Ability levels may range from severe and profoundly impaired to mildly affected. In this book, we focus on children with ASD who learned to talk and whose cognitive abilities developed into the typical or gifted range.

The social and communication behaviour of individuals with ASD differs from that of most people. These differences are caused by differences in the way the brain develops from very early in life. The result is a different way of experiencing the world, which is not well understood by most people unaffected by ASD. Thus, when individuals with and without ASD interact, there is an incongruity that neither party readily understands or is immediately equipped to resolve. This can lead to tensions, awkwardness and ultimately rejection and loneliness for individuals with ASD. As the world gains insight into the minds of individuals with ASD, a new appreciation for individual differences will emerge. Once demystified, the different preferences, interests, behaviours, reactions and perspectives of individuals with ASD will be valued and embraced. Rather than judging the individual with ASD as odd or rude or even inferior in some way, we can strive to understand and support the information processing and life success of individuals with ASD. In this book, we take a step towards bridging the gap between the world of ASD and neurotypical individuals by providing the reader with a glimpse into the mind of children with ASD.

What exactly is ASD?

By their first birthday, children with ASD have begun to distinguish themselves from other children. They begin to display differences in communication, social and play development. Some children also begin to display differences in their ability to adjust to unexpected changes in routine and by occasionally moving their bodies in unusual or repetitive ways. When these differences interfere with children's ability to learn in the usual way and to develop the skills expected for their age, a developmental assessment by an expert in child development is needed. The results of the assessment will indicate whether or not the child meets the criteria for an ASD or could benefit from special therapeutic or educational services. Socially, children with ASD usually do not seek out interaction with others simply for the purpose of being together or sharing the moment. Once engaged with someone, children with ASD do not display the expected range of strategies for continuing the interaction. They seem unaware of how to link their behaviour to that of others during play with toys, in social games, in use of spoken language, or even in matching the mood of others. The result is a disruption in the natural to-and-fro, or reciprocity, of interaction between two people.

One important aspect of development that is altered in individuals with ASD is imitation. Imitation is an important aspect of social development that enables children to learn from others and also to develop the perspective about how two people are alike and different. Learning through imitation does not emerge in the expected way for children with ASD. They don't seem to notice the behavioural nuances of others and try to duplicate the socially relevant behaviours (like how to play with a new toy or how to pretend that a box can be a shoe). Imitation of others' actions is not used to "share in the moment" or join in the spirit of an activity with others. If children with ASD do imitate others, it often seems more like disconnected mimicry rather than a playful interactive exchange of relatedness. Through special instruction, children with ASD usually do learn to imitate others but sometimes the timing and appropriateness of what they choose to imitate may be awkward or unusual.

Individuals with ASD generally show difficulty with social insight and have difficulty with perspective taking. As a result, children with ASD are not socially savvy, and they often say or do things that are notably inappropriate or unexpected in the situation at hand. They may be considered overly forthright in their comments, "telling it like it is", which can be embarrassing to parents and offensive to some people. For example, a child with ASD may announce that the meal at someone's house tastes bad, or that someone's dress is ugly. Such comments are not meant to be hurtful. It's just that the child with ASD lacks understanding of social rules prohibiting the statement of potentially hurtful things, and lacks the perspective-taking skills to enable him or her to know that the person wearing the dress likes it and thinks it looks nice. They also have difficulty using subtlety and humour to convey criticism or differences of opinion.

Recognising others' emotions and spontaneously sharing their own emotions are also difficult for individuals with ASD. They have difficulty "reading" people's body language, including facial expressions, and inferring how others might be feeling. Trying to understand the source of someone's emotion and expressing empathy are even more difficult for a child with ASD. Thus, the person with ASD may say or do things that have not taken into account others' emotional states, or emotional history. For example, a child with ASD may never have learned that certain topics or behaviours upset a particular individual. And when the child performs the undesired behaviour or discusses the taboo topic in front of this individual, they are sincerely surprised and perhaps even hurt at the person's reaction. The social difficulties associated with ASD can significantly curtail the formation of friendships, cause difficulty on the job, and give rise to social anxiety.

Communication is another aspect of development that is disrupted in ASD. Some children with ASD never learn to speak. Others develop some spoken language, but are always significantly impaired in their ability to formulate their ideas into age-appropriate grammatical structures and in their ability to comprehend what others say. Still, other children with ASD develop complex, even gifted, language abilities and may even sound like the "little professor" because they use such advanced vocabulary and complex sentence structures. Yet even some of the linguistically gifted individuals with ASD have difficulties understanding and producing non-verbal communication, as in use of gestures, facial expressions, other body language and tone of voice, to effectively convey the intended meaning of their messages to others. Then there is the matter of how best to shift the topic of the conversation, how to share the conversational floor, and how to show others that you are interested in what they are saying by extending the topic of their choice. As you may guess, having a conversation with other people is likely to be hard work for a person with ASD. They have to concentrate hard on figuring out what their conversational partner is really saying, and read between the lines so that they may plan a relevant response. After all, most people don't really say what they mean. And then there is the task of translating their own ideas into sentences and sequences of thoughts that will make sense to their conversational partner.

A particular area of communication difficulty for verbal individuals with ASD is comprehension and production of spoken or written language that is figurative rather than literal in nature. Conversation, humour, books, movies and advertisements have many figures of speech. Children with ASD require more time to think through and understand anything that is not literal. Therefore, they often are late in "getting the point" and are late in responding. They may begin to laugh at a joke after everyone else has already finished laughing and the topic has been shifted to something else. This puts the child with ASD out of step with other children and may lead to increased risk for teasing and even bullying. Children with ASD also have difficulty "reading between the lines" or inferring what others mean. Often, people leave out bits of information when they are talking or writing a message, and they rely on their listener to infer what they are really trying to say. While listening to someone talking or deciphering the meaning of a text message or email, we are simultaneously forming ideas about whether the speaker is saying exactly what they mean or whether they are implying a different meaning. We must decipher their intended meaning quickly if we are to respond appropriately. For the person with ASD, difficulty understanding unstated (inferred or implied) meaning within others' messages often leads to misunderstandings, sometimes to the point of frustration for both conversational partners.

Another aspect of language processing is the ability to integrate all of the messages that have been expressed during a conversation, or in a book, or in a movie, to get the main point or gist. This ability is hard-won for most individuals with ASD, who do much better at remembering minute details rather than formulating the main idea. Thus, when asked to give a snapshot of what someone else said, or what a book was about, the individual with ASD may have great difficulty giving a succinct summary and may instead provide several quotes from the person or book. In the teen years, the communication difficulties associated with ASD pose particular challenges, especially when it comes to dating. Knowing just how to invite someone on a date, and then using one's communication and social skills to make sure the date is enjoyable for both people is not easy for the person with ASD, so an extra dose of understanding, patience and coaching are in order.

Some children with ASD are very sensitive to experiences involving touch, taste, smell, hearing or sight. Some may be bothered by subtle sounds, such as the buzzing of fluorescent lights, which most people do not even notice. They may be bothered by the texture of certain fabrics and refuse to wear clothing made of that fabric, or indicate that having their hair brushed is very painful. Certain wavelengths of light may be quite uncomfortable, and some adults with ASD prefer to wear sunglasses for this reason even when indoors. Alternatively, children with ASD may be unusually insensitive to certain sensory experiences. For example, they may have a very high tolerance for pain, or fail to react when a very loud sound occurs nearby. In addition, some children with ASD show unusual interests in certain types of sensory experience. For example, they may frequently smell objects, watch moving parts of objects (e.g. spinning the wheels on a toy car or watching a fan), or watch flashes of light.

In addition to the difficulties above, children with ASD often prefer routine and have a limited range of interests or activities. They may even become intensely focused on special topics, some of which may be quite out of the ordinary. As you reflect on the images presented in this book, you will guess some of the special interests of the children whose lives are shared with you here. Sometimes the level of technical knowledge or artistic ability is surprising, given the child's apparent challenges in other aspects of development. And despite the level of expertise that shows itself in children's drawings, musical performances, quantitative thinking or mechanical savvy, many individuals with ASD have difficulty expanding and generalising these special abilities to solve practical or scientific challenges. Thus, they may not be able to establish productive employment using their talents.

Now that you have become acquainted with the specific challenges faced by individuals with ASD, I hope that you will take a moment to indulge yourself in the images within this book. These images permit a glimpse into the minds of children with ASD. These minds are not imperfect, as Chase tells us in his personal account of experiencing the world through autism. Rather, their minds are different. As you will see when you read about Chase's experiences, the way that we react to another person has a profound impact on their sense of self and this impact affects their wellbeing for a lifetime. Like everyone else, people with ASD need love, encouragement and acceptance. The experience of love, encouragement and acceptance must be present early in life, and be consistent throughout life or else a person is likely to develop a sense that they don't belong or are not valued. Chase poignantly explains how important it is to be understood and embraced by others. And yet so often, being understood and embraced is not the experience of a person with ASD. Little do people realise how hard a child with ASD works at navigating this complex world through a neurobiologically different perceptual and conceptual system. Each achievement is worthy of acknowledgment and quiet celebration. May we all remember this as we encounter a child, teen or adult who stops us in our tracks because they differ from our expectations or from our comfort zone. May we take a moment to pause before we judge and may we be more free with our words of encouragement. It is our choice, after all, to speak words that uplift rather than criticize.

May you come away inspired by the children whose lives are shared with us through this book. They do indeed march to the beat of a different drummer. I hope that in our next encounter with someone whose behaviour resembles that described above, we pause to take in the gift being delivered to us. May we open the gift by listening, observing and trying to expand our own expectations to make room for the unique individual before us. And if we dare to accept the invitation, our dance will become a little more nuanced, a little more delicate and much more engaged with life in all its majesty.

Dr. Rebecca Landa
The founder and director of the Center for Autism and Related Disorders (CARD)
and the REACH research program at the Kennedy Krieger Institute
Professor of Psychiatry at Johns Hopkins University School of Medicine

the children

Magnus

"many school professionals told me that Magnus's IQ was below average…"

My "slow", "borderline" son Magnus
is now a member of MENSA!

JP

He replied, "It's Jacqueline Roque – beautiful."

After all, it really does not matter whether he was within the spectrum or not.

Snow

Snow is spectacular

Listen!

It sounds like maracas falling down a tree if you touch it.

Snow is fabulous

Look!

I see little bits of ice cream coming down to the ground.

Snow is superb

Touch it!

It feels like a slippery block of ice sliding over my hand.

Smell it!

It's like fluffy cotton wool.

Snow is fantastic

Taste it!

It's like ice cubes sliding down your throat.

My opinion on robots

I think robots are fantastic because they can carry on work easily and because they don't need to go to the toilet at all or have lunch or a drink or even to go to bed. A robot can work tremendously fast and because they are already programmed they can do everything that they are supposed to do.

I think robots are cool because they could do almost anything such as play Ping-Pong or move about when they are playing music or roll sideways. I think robots are fabulous because they could do jobs that are hard for humans. These jobs include things like welding, spraying paint and making cars. Robots can also do jobs that are really boring for humans like screwing in bolts.

I think robots are interesting because they come in all shapes and sizes and in different colours. Some robots are different to others. Different robots are used for different jobs.

I think robots are going to be fascinating in the future because there are already lots of different kinds of robots. In the future maybe robots are going to be on wheels or on rocket boosters. They might be used to drive cars or to serve food.

Benjamin

…he began coming home from his after-school care with detailed schematics: tyres, axles, driveshafts, linkages, engines, transmissions, pipes, wires, rivets, weld marks, lines I couldn't decipher but knew were there…

…then everything changed with his first "human body" anatomy book… He drew the body systems. The circulatory system branched out from the heart through the thickest arteries to the smallest capillaries, filling the shape of the body with flowing, pumping blood: blue supply, red return…

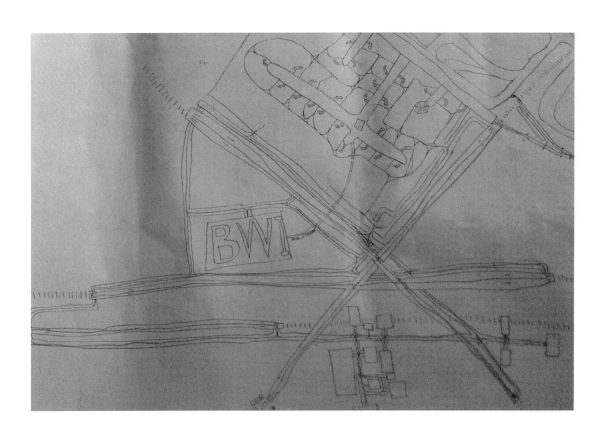

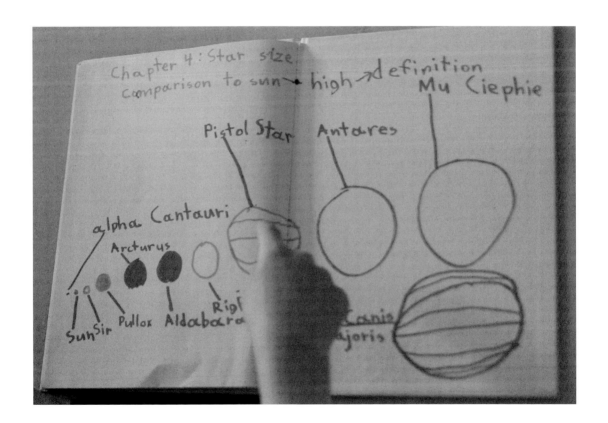

Chapter 4: Star size, comparison to sun → high → definition

alpha Cantauri
Arcturus
Pistol Star
Antares
Mu Ciephie

Sun Sir Pullox Aldabara Rigl

Canis ajoris

47

James

Saturday Nov 1 2008
12:00 am
12:01 am
12:02 am
12:03 am
12:04 am
12:05 am
12:06 am
12:07 am
12:08 am
12:09 am
12:10 am
12:11 am
12:12 am
12:13 am
12:14 am
12:15 am

12:21 am
12:22 am
12:23 am
12:24 am
12:25 am
12:26 am
12:27 am
12:28 am
12:29 am
12:30 am
12:31 am
12:32 am
12:33 am
12:34 am
12:35 am
12:36 am

12:42 am
12:43 am
12:44 am
12:45 am
12:46 am
12:47 am
12:48 am
12:49 am
12:50 am
12:51 am
12:52 am
12:53 am
12:54 am
12:55 am
12:56 am
12:57 am
12:58 am
12:59 am

1:04 am
1:05 am
1:06 am
1:07 am
1:08 am
1:09 am
1:10 am
1:11 am
1:12 am
1:13 am
1:14 am
1:15 am
1:16 am
1:17 am
1:18 am

1:28
1:29
1:30
1:31
1:32
1:33
1:34

53

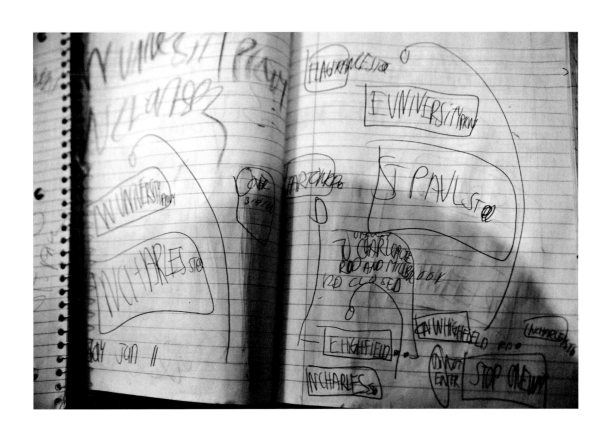

55

We are having a great time in Italy – just to let you know!! We have been visiting towns and we have been walking around places. I am getting flipped out because I don't want to walk around too much! On Saturday we went to this villa with a really nice pool and a really nice basement! I am OBSESSED with the lights that are yellow and they are REALLY beautiful! I have been nervous that there is no piano anywhere to visit here because I REALLY wanted to play beautifully – Swan Lake on it. I love to play it at Shari's house in New York because I think the note sounds sound awesome! Because I like that it is high. On Friday I slept till 9:00 and Saturday till 9:50 – OMG I think that that's the latest time that I've ever woke up at!!! On Wednesday the 17th we left to go. At 3:25 we got to the airport. Our flight was at 5:15. Guess what they had in the plane – A TV screen that shows you what movies to watch and what CDs to listen to. The next day our flight was like 11:30 in the morning! And we had to wait a very long time in the airport until the plane came. Something showed you what time the planes left. We had to walk for a REALLY long time on Friday to explore Rome. There was lots of things there that I saw. I saw the Colosseum there. I went to sleep at 11:15 on Friday night and I woke up at 1:00 the next morning before I woke up at 9:50. That's the end of the note!!

Alex and Ben

Ben's love of lighthouses could be an "obsession" or "perseveration"…

So many of Alex's fears are based not on real factors so much as they are a vestige of his communication disorder and his need for sticking to safe routines.

(Alex said,) "I AM NOT GOING UP!"

"My proudest moment was when I climbed the lighthouse. I got over my fear. I know I can try new things now even if they scare me at first."
(from Alex's journal)

interviewing Chase

Dr. Landa introduced me to Chase, a young Autism activist who speaks at conferences.

He openly shared his knowledge and experiences and discussed what sort of challenges a child with ASD would have while growing up and his tips to make their lives happier. On the following pages are some excerpts from our conversations over last two years.

ABOUT DIAGNOSIS AND REACTION

MAKIKO: *When and how did you find out your diagnosis?*
CHASE: I was like six. Probably younger. Around that time my parents got divorced due to my Dad's inability to get his bipolar disorder under a doctor's care. Part of that has led to a constant internal need for me to make sure that I am pursuing all avenues of treatment for any issues that I feel like are beyond my control. I got to know Autism by definition and saw books piling up at home. Now I know what is going on. Out of finding out more about the disorder with books and frustration with my parents' reactions to my behaviour, I internalised immediately that there was something wrong with me. Out of that came a persistent, life-long-lasting thought that I was somehow less than human. That my own existence was flawed and thus a mistake. I carried that wherever I went, whether it was visiting my father in a different state, school, or being home alone with my sister.

When I was in the first grade, four or five (children) sitting together and working, I had to explain why I could not do that because I was autistic. But they thought I was "artistic". It was frustrating. Out of incidents like these, and the persistent feeling that I am a mistake, there is this need for perfection in all of my actions because I often feel like I straddle the cusp of being socially accepted and if I were to maintain some perfect manner to my actions then I would be accepted or at least be given some level of respect. I saw the rest of the world, be it my family or my academic environment, seeing me as a mistake, non-deserving of respect and if I were to fail in my actions then I would be completely cast aside altogether and be forever deemed undeserving in friendship and love.

M: *At that time you were in a mainstream school?*

C: Yes, a mainstream school. It was just the beginning.

SOCIAL MARGINALISATION

M: *Being autistic made you sad?*

C: No, there is so much for being autistic, more about how people react about it. It's all about people's reaction (to Autism). As much as I strive for perfection in my life, there are things about the way I live life differently from those around me that I come to accept and try to be proud of, but often it is difficult because people don't know how to react to my emotional and sensory needs and deficits.

M: *People means adults?*

C: People in general. Kids and adults. Even a family for that matter. One of the big things is that lots of people trying to explain that ultimately what they have to say about Autism is not like a theme of the paper and not separate from it. This is their lens of reality. It's their lens – the fundamental thing. How they apply the "perception of thoughts" on what Autism is. It is not separate from a person. It is a person although there is infinite spectrum. With that, for the longest time, I came to believe that mere possession of the diagnosis wasn't my fault and it was the world around me. As I have become older, I've come to accept the reality that it is nobody's fault at all – fault is ultimately a non-factor because the diagnosis was purely cosmic chance. And with that came the thought that all the marginalisation that I experience is not out of some malignant force operating through the people around me, but rather systemic. It is a reflection of the world around me and that with that, I came to accept that we are all victims of a system that continues to marginalise those who could become our best and our brightest. Out of that conclusion, I have come to wrestle harder with a dangerous line of thought that I am often scared to talk about; that for the past decade or so there has been a constant suicidality that catches me on a near-daily basis that can often keep me from striving to achieve my best and often the "perfection" I strive to achieve so I can move off the cusp and become socially accepted.

Out of learning and accepting that the nature of my existence is cosmic chance, I have felt liberated in a way where I can sincerely accept and forgive my inability to be perfect. However, with that, I struggle with the thought that now that I see myself and the marginalisation I experience as systemic, I feel like it becomes a charade and now that I see it as an act, a seemingly, permanently false representation of the world around me, that somehow I am entitled to opt out of it. I also have this persistent thought that though I am receiving the best treatment I could possibly have (both my psychologist and my psychiatrist have been incredibly valuable in maintaining my success), so I deserve to feel guilty for needing treatment just to cope and survive the world around me and without the medicine, I would not be able to survive. So the treatment, coupled with my own perceptions, fuels this idea that somehow I myself am a mistake. It takes daily effort to get over this and the things I can do to measure my own success. For me, I've come to learn the value of goal-setting and achieving those goals has been valuable for me. That in part has been helped also by my treatment.

…Then I thought, "I don't have to do all these battles." I can just go and benefit other people with all the knowledge. I choose to keep going, though the temptation to stop going waxes and wanes. I hope I can eventually come to make a difference in those around me, especially the younger generation that can benefit more from the advancements in treatments and interventions that can make a real, palpable difference for the better.

ABOUT FRIENDSHIP

M: *Have you been feeling isolated or do you have friends*?

C: I do have friends. I have friends I am immensely close with. Lots of time I feel like going back as much as I do and I enjoy spending a great time together having all kinds of adventures and everything else… Then I feel like it was kind of a long time and I think "Okay, what did I do wrong this time?" Looking back, I have not really enjoyed social life but I was thinking about "What did I do wrong?" Not only to friends but to everyone in the family as well. That's kind of like a major driving question and eventually came to a conclusion that things actually matter to me – I don't have to have their approval and I don't have to have the same, I can't – how I value myself, who I am and where I am going. I feel a lot more degraded on purpose… especially Autism – how it affects me. With different voids, I don't have to play rules to make me feel lonely. I will go out and find all the excitement outside on my own – it actually matters to me. I've come to accept that the consistent mantra of "What did I do wrong" hurts more than it benefits, and I have to have the courage to say what I feel, the tact to deliver it with a manner of kindness, and the ability to have my thoughts engaged or contested. I feel like it is the only way I can go about life. And even more importantly, I've come to accept that conversations of serious weight are to be done in person or through a medium where you can read someone's body language (i.e. Skype) and engagement. When people say heavy thoughts that could have serious consequences over a written medium, they often lose a sense of gravity – that is essential.

M: *Do you have any friends who have similar symptoms?*

C: I do have a few friends with autism spectrum. It is interesting to see their ways of coping with the world around them and the often parallel choices we end up making.

M: *Do you have any true believers in you? Someone you can go back to and ask for support whenever you like?*

C: Yes. It is tough to find people for that. A friend in D.C. – our past is different but we value similar things and we have very good connections.

INTERESTS/JOINING A LARGE GROUP

M: *What did you like to study when you were at primary or middle school level?*

C: History and Math… and I have perfect pitch in music… absolutely perfect pitch but lacking a sense of rhythm.

M: *Do you play any instruments?*

C: I played cello for about eight years. I am not good at it.

M: *Why?*

C: I did not practice as much as others did. With virtually no sense of rhythm. And playing a large instrument required large degree of finesse. Luckily I am left-handed and hit the right note and at the same time my right hand, the bow hand, could not grip the bow properly. I could create my own way to do rhythm.

M: *Do you have perfect melody in your brain but your body can't realise that, which causes frustration?*

C: Not so much. Pitches are there. I know what the pitches are, I know where the order is going. It's about next sequence. Like what time A goes to B and B goes to C.

M: My child really wanted to learn guitar. He is also left-handed but his teacher did not provide him with a guitar for left-handed people. So he tried to learn with it. He does not have good motor skills and it was not easy to hold it. While he has perfect sounds in his brain, however, his fingers could not realise the sounds he wanted.

C: It is inevitable but a kid who can read music, his body can't move to it – I would suggest voice lessons. I realised I had perfect pitch when I was sophomore in high school, already playing cello for six years. I could have joined the choir… but it was too late.

M: *Did you play on your own or as part of a group?*

C: I was part of the orchestra.

M: *Did you struggle joining a large group, like the orchestra?*

C: I was in the class and this was how I built up friends. At a time certain reactions became strange. Their misunderstanding. A clear lack of communication… I guess on my part and their part…

A PLAN FROM NOW ON

M: *What are you planning to do now? Why you are learning Sociology? Why did you choose it?*

C: It is close to what I am actually interested in. Right now I don't feel school is right for me… it has not been right for a long time. What I want to do is what I am actually going to do with my life.

M: *Do you have any obsessions? In good ways or bad ways?*

C: I am spiritual person. Spiritual life comes into my mind… I am obsessed with that direction. (I thought about) the meaning of ME and how I can use my knowledge to help other people. All the things I learnt, the best way for me to approach my life is with an ideal basis, a process called "ego deconstruction" – things you have done don't really matter. Very powerful if it takes place. Shifting focus off myself down to larger ideas. Giving up ME and seeing what happens. Giving is rewarding in itself. It is to cherish happiness as it is fleeting and comes like seasons, and that I am merely a set of ideas. Sometimes those ideas take form and conglomerate themselves, and sometimes they are scattered, thus leaving me detached from the world around me to experience my inner self more deeply. I believe that while no one can define my life other than me, and thus not to create heavy attachments to a particular person or idea (or even ideal), I still need everyone in some form or another. This is largely in part of the reality that without the contrast of the lives around me, I have no frame of reference for my own existence and without that frame of reference, I get into a dangerous mantra that leads back to my suicidality.

M: *What makes you happy?*

C: I have gone through immense worries to give up all things. I am given opportunities to speak here in front of you to share things that matter and ideas get passed on to other people. This is my job. I inspire people. I just tell them to think about this direction. "Here is the direction, you go with it." Inspire people to get them where they need to. At the end of the day, a question is the God, how do you connect (to it) absolutely beyond yourself, establish the connection? How I could get people, regardless of Autism or not…

M: *Any words for children with ASD?*

C: ABA is a good therapy for ages two to six. A tailored curriculum may just be the single best way to reach someone on the spectrum, otherwise they will never see the utility in maintaining important aspects of living such as exercise and hygiene. And learning what it means to value yourself, while living in a reality that consistently teaches you that you have less value than those around you, is essential. However, it can't be done alone. Everyone needs help on the journey of life, but some need it more than others – and there is absolutely nothing wrong with that. Everybody starts the journey with assets and deficits that are different from everybody else, but regardless, the journey is something to be cherished, perhaps even more than we (especially me) can realise in the moment. Make believe therapy would work. I would ask parents to try using a metaphor. You know a metaphor more than a kid does. Communicate through a metaphor and set that metaphor into reality. If a kid is interested in *Star Wars*, *Jedi* and I teach him/her things through the lens of *Star Wars*… and bring them more and more into reality. Also teach him/her basic self identity – who he/she is and the difference from his/her core age. Help him/her value a human being teaching from early age. They absolutely love to do it. "Next pirate, next knight…" Go in costumes and teach kids how to value themselves.

And out of the act of truly giving a piece of yourself with the intention of making someone's life consistently better, as a result is something truly precious. And despite my own struggles, helping add joy and meaning to those around me is consistently my highest priority. There are grim realities about life on the spectrum, but to experience life and to utilise "my intellectual being" is something that I must continue to believe is worth it. With that, if I had to give parents and loved ones something that could help the loved ones they know on the spectrum, it is to foster an environment that meets their emotional needs (and if you don't know what they are, ask and find out what they are) and primes them in a way that they can succeed and feel the sincerity of their own successes and forgive themselves for any mistakes along the way. Again, I've come to accept that the journey isn't something to be done alone – it's a shared experience that is only going to get bigger and brighter – as long as I choose for it to get bigger and brighter.

On my bedroom mantelpiece, I keep a quote from *Paradise Lost* that deals with the nature of suicidality against forces much bigger than the individual:

"To be no more. Sad cure! for who would lose,
Though full of pain, this intellectual being,
Those thoughts that wander through eternity,
To perish rather, swallowed up and lost
In the wide womb of uncreated night,
Devoid of sense and motion?"

John Milton, Book Two, Lines 146-150

To me, it represents the internal fight that with the idea of a quiet senseless (as in non-perception) non-existence comes the loss of what it means to live a thoughtful life. I realise I shouldn't keep such things like this on a bedroom mantelpiece, but to deny this reality would be disingenuous to the struggles I will continue to face.

Here are the full texts from the parents, which support the photo essays in "the children". I included some milestones for children, which will help us understand more.

Magnus

My son, Magnus, is a master builder. Starting at a very young age, he would build elaborate structures in our living room, out of anything he could get his hands on. He had the uncanny ability to look at an object, whether it be a structure, animal or insect, and recreate it using LEGO and other building toys. The accuracy and detail displayed in his creations was nothing short of shocking – especially considering the fact that he could not speak until the age of five, and was unable to follow simple directions. Many school professionals told me that Magnus's IQ was below average, and used words like "slow" and "borderline" to describe him. I was well aware that my child was different; not like most. But I never thought for one moment that he was "slow". Finally, I took Magnus to a psychologist for intelligence testing. It took several days as clinicians worked to unlock the mystery of his mind, administering test after test. The results? An autism diagnosis, and the revelation of superior intellect. And guess what? My "slow", "borderline" son Magnus is now a member of MENSA!

Milestones:

0-5 years: non-verbal.

1 year old: doing 100-piece puzzles.

2 years old: doing 500-piece puzzles.

4-5 years old: able to recreate animals and insects with LEGO.

9 years old: started taking mathematics lessons for the gifted at a leading university.

12 years old: reading 5th grade level although he was told that he would never read before. Learning mathematics from a PhD student in Applied Mathematics.

Information about his photo essays:

The MENSA card in the chapter is not a current one. Magnus renewed his membership and holds a new card.

JP

Love for Picasso

Since JP had never had any "therapies" before, we were apprehensive about relocating and sending him to the KKI. We were very nervous – all we needed was to escape in Paris, one of our favourite cities, for a while.

One afternoon, I took him to Le Marais, one of the oldest quarters in town. He came along with his instant camera. We visited Musée Picasso. In an open space with several black metal sculptures, he started clicking. This is one of the photos he took. He was only four years old.

As he was excited, he started running around to take a quick look. For the second round, I started showing him various stages of Picasso's works. He did not say much but nodded and smiled. After visiting the top floor, we started going downstairs. He pointed at Baboon and Young and smiled. He said nothing but I

Milestones:

2 years old: already reading books in two languages; solving 96-piece jigsaw puzzles on his own in 10-15 minutes.

3 years old: worked with Montessori materials designed for 6 year olds.

4 years old: started taking therapies at the KKI. Until then he did not speak. Within 6 months, he caught up from a 2 year delay in speech.

9 years old: started learning mathematics from a mathematician from a leading university.

noticed he loved it. We went downstairs and he spotted animated bullfighting pictures were being projected on the screen. We sat down on one of the steps and watched them for a long time.

One term later, we went back to Paris again. JP asked me to take him back to Musée Picasso "because he always liked it". As we walked around, he told us the names of the ladies in the portraits – he knew all the names of Picasso's lovers chronologically. In front of Portrait of Jacqueline Roque with Arms Crossed, he took a chair and looked at it for a while. He turned his head and smiled. I asked, "Who is it?" He replied, "It's Jaqueline Roque – beautiful." Then continued looking on the ground floor and found a large bullhead. He said that it was funny and asked me to take photos of it with him. After visiting upstairs, we walked downstairs and JP was happy to find his favorite Baboon and Young again. "I like it. This monkey has a car head! Look, Mommy!" This time he could express what he thought about it. I smiled back to him.

Information about his photo essays:

4 years old: a photo of Picasso's sculptures, taken by himself.
5 years old: two images of himself, face painted black for drama.
8 years old: started playing Judo and it brought him more self-esteem and confidence. Water birds photo, Snow poem, and My opinion on robots were made at the same time.

Benjamin

How Stuff Works

Just after his sixth birthday, Benjamin began to explore how stuff works. With his entry into kindergarten came school bus rides, and the driver of Bus 64 tolerated Benjamin's eccentricities and the delays they caused. He made it a habit to stick his head under the bus and look around before boarding each morning. He'd save his mind's picture until late afternoon when he could get paper and coloured pencils or markers, and he began coming home from his after-school care with detailed schematics: tyres, axles, driveshafts, linkages, engines, transmissions, pipes, wires, rivets, weld marks, lines I couldn't decipher but knew were there.

On weekends, he asked me to pop the hood to my car, and his smile spread as he took in the compartment. "What's that?" The engine. "What's that?" The coolant. "What's that?" Oil filter. "What's that?" I don't know. "That?" I don't know; I'll get the manual. He went inside and drew it all.

Milestones

2 – 2½ years old: regressed from saying 10-12 words to completely non-verbal and non-social.

2¾ years old: began therapy at the KKI – his vocabulary passed his typical peers before he turned 4.

6 years old: could draw the human anatomy and explain all major body systems; discovered Google, Google Earth, and YouTube; the rest of these are self-discovered from internet searches.

7 years old: could locate most major international airports on a globe and draw their runway configurations from memory.

8 years old: could precisely draw and explain all 4 stages of gas turbine aircraft engines, including air and fuel flow; could discuss nuclear fusion taking place in star models, including what elements are produced at each star layer depending on mass and age of stars; could tell all about the planets and their various moons, and began investigating the concept of galaxies beyond our own as well as the broad expanse of the universe.

Walking back to the car from swimming class or shopping was a half-hour ordeal, as he poked his head under every car along the way, and held his hand out to stop cars, which slowed.

And when the visible became mundane, he drew the inside of the engine, as best as he could imagine: spark plugs with lightning bolts, pipes with crazy-angled joints, cables wrapping around layers of gears, extending out to nowhere. He combined styles, the underside of his bus connecting to a cut-away of the engine compartment, details filling large sheets of poster-board and easel paper.

Then everything changed with his first "human body" anatomy book. Body system after system revealed itself in full-colour transparent overlays. He turned the pages and stared, until he reached the schematic of embryonic growth, at which time he put the book down in the corner of the room and refused to touch it for several days.

He drew the body systems. The circulatory system branched out from the heart through the thickest arteries to the smallest capillaries, filling the shape

Information about his photo essays:

5 years old: text How Stuff Works was written; drew undersides of cars and Bus 64

6 years old: human anatomy

7 years old: BWI map

8 years old: stars

Amtrack gave us permission to use partial images of an Amtrack train, platforms, train tracks, etc. at Union Station, Washington D.C in this chapter.

All the drawings are properties of the parents and the reproduction right of the texts is reserved to them.

of the body within the flowing, pumping blood: blue supply, red return.

Other body systems didn't fill the human outline. They left white space in the arms or legs which needed to be filled, so that when the oesophagus, stomach, small intestines, and large intestines fit into the centre of the figure, pipes and cables extended out into the extremities meeting working gears at the joints, and the body shape became the most wonderful Human / Bus 64 Cyborg imaginable.

He thumbed the book every night. " What's that?" The liver. "What's that?" Kidneys. "What's that?" I don't know, Ben. "Daddy, it's the Duodenum."

For Valentine's Day, his kindergarten class drew hearts. His heart included chambers and ventricles, wrapped in arteries and veins, complete with an aortic arch. Someday, some girl will get a Valentine's heart and will ask him, "What's that?" And Benjamin will fall in love.

James

CALENDAR

My son James has a calendar imprinted on his brain. Not surprising, as he spends hours looking at calendars, flipping through the months, forward and back, and writing his own calendars in the dozens of composition notebooks he keeps on our kitchen table. You want to buy James a present? Forget toys – a date book will do it. The calendar on my iPhone is his nirvana…

Two years ago, James' obsession with numbers mutated into this fixation with dates, days, months, time of day – and it, combined with his awe-inspiring memory, makes for many a jaw-dropping moment. James remembers every thing we've done in the last two years, and the day, date and time we did it. When random people tell him their birthday, he tells them what day of the week it was on – last year – and this year. There is no processing time during which he computes this information – he just spits it

Milestones

14 months old: already knew names of shapes like trapezoid and octagon, however, did not say "mama".

2 years old: started writing letters and numbers obsessively.

3 years old: discovered he had perfect pitch; was playing a simple 2 handed version of "Pachelbel's Canon" on the piano.

4 years old: could count by 13s and do advanced mathematical sequence problems; reading every word he saw.

Information about his photo essays:

4 years old: Calendar was written.

8 years old: street and heart drawings.

9 years old: the paragraph about his trip to Italy was written.

All the drawings are properties of the parent and the reproduction right of the texts is reserved to her.

out, instantly. On the first day of every month, James wakes up with a bigger smile than usual. "It's a new month!!!" he exclaims gleefully, the second he opens his eyes. The joy is so pure. Imagine deriving such pleasure from such a simple thing – and getting to experience that delight twelve times a year. We should all be that lucky…

Alex and Ben

Beacons of Hope

Despite the fact that I am roughly 2,900 days post autism diagnosis, I admit that when Autism Speaks finally made available the 100-day kit for newly diagnosed families, I was curious to see what had been developed for neophyte autism families. Eight years ago when we were told that my son Alex had an autism spectrum disorder (PDD-NOS), the resources on autism that were available were scattered across the internet in an incoherent fashion. In those early, dark days, not only did I have to deal with the rollercoaster of emotions that follow a diagnosis, but inside that chaos I somehow had to develop an action plan for something I knew nothing about and still hoped wasn't true. The only solace I took when my younger son Ben's diagnosis came about less than two years later was, "At least I know now what I need to do." The diagnostic and intervention wheels turn much more quickly the second time around because the action plan is burned into your brain.

As I perused the new materials online last year, I ran across a statement that was new to me. It was so startling that I actually cut it out and placed it in my Google window. As the returns came back confirming the validity this titbit of information, I realised that even seven years into the autism journey, I can learn something new about this condition that has taken over our lives so completely.

Knowing my husband was on a train headed home with his BlackBerry in hand, I shot him a quick e-mail:

"Look what I pulled from the Autism Speaks 100-day kit: 'For example, a child with autism might be _obsessed_ with learning all about vacuum cleaners, train schedules, or _lighthouses'._"

Joe's response was nearly immediate: "Really? Lighthouses? On par with vacuums and train schedules? And here I thought that they were just a pleasant diversion."

Our family's passion for lighthouses began innocently enough with a trip to Barnegat, New Jersey in the summer of 2005. Having been invited down to the shore house of good friends for the day, our hosts suggested a trip to visit the local lighthouse.

Why Ben was so attracted to "Old Barney" is still a mystery to me. He made a beeline straight to the door and flew up the stairs quickly; my husband scarcely had time to catch up. Alex was extremely afraid of heights at the time, and refused to make the climb. Not particularly thrilled with the notion myself, I was more than happy to sit this little adventure out.

My persistent Ben was not going to give up on me so easily. Having flown down the stairs as quickly as he had flown up, at the base of the Barnegat Lighthouse, he announced he wanted to go up again.

Looking at me pointedly, my husband said, "Your turn."

"I'm not going up there!" I said.

"Come on, Mommy, come on!" and with that Ben was back through the door, beginning a second ascent.

As I attempted to keep up with my fearless son ahead of me, my stomach churned with each vibration of the metal staircase under my feet. What propelled me up those stairs, my knuckles turning white as I gripped the banisters so tightly, was more of concern about being a step behind him when he got to the top so I could pull him back from the edge before he flew off. Autism is not for the weak-hearted. My personal discomfort here was irrelevant. I managed to grab Ben by the arm before he got to the door to the observation deck.

"Wait for me," I said.

I took a deep breath, and we passed through the door together. I immediately backed us against the structure behind me. The wind was whipping ferociously and it felt as though we might be blown off the top. My legs were still shaking from the stress of the climb and I felt slightly nauseated.

"It's not windy on the other side," Ben told me as he began pulling my arm. With my back still pressed to the wall, I eased my way to the far side of the deck, and once the wind was off of us, I had a chance to look at my son; and to look out at the ocean and share in what he saw.

Magic.

His beaming smile indicated nothing but pure joy to me. It was infectious. That moment was worth more than the fear I had overcome to get to this magical place with Ben. For a moment, we were connected by the intensity of his experience, the joy he was sharing with such startling ease. It was hard to remain afraid of something that had captivated my boy so totally. These are the moments I live for with my boys. As elusive as they can be, these connections are possible. As rare as they are, they are that much sweeter when they do happen.

Autism is full of words with negative connotations. Obsession and perseveration are two of them. When we speak of obsessions or perseverations, we tend to link these words with behaviours that separate our children from us. Whether it's the way our sons might line up their race cars or trains so methodically, never allowing us to disturb their order or let us in to engage in play with them. Or perhaps it's the way the bedtime ritual must be played out, night after night, with no omissions or changes in order, with the hope that if we do not deviate, perhaps everyone can get a good night's sleep for a change.

I never knew that lighthouses were a known area of special interest for people with autism. I admit difficulty in accepting that Ben's love of lighthouses could be an "obsession" or "perseveration". I have always viewed it as a "passion". His interest in them has enriched all of our lives. We have had far, far too many moments of emotional connection with both of our sons as we have travelled up and down the East Coast, from Sandy Hook to Ocracoke, looking for a new perspective, a new ocean's view, a new set of steps to climb, and more facts to add to our collective knowledge of these shining beacons that are so rich with our American history.

Even Alex is now able to enjoy the climbs, though overcoming his fears about the lighthouses was not easy. They, too, are significantly important to him for very different reasons.

Alex crossed the threshold with us at Old Cape Henry in Virginia Beach the next summer, in July 2006. We were visiting my in-laws and decided to take an early morning climb before the day's heat (forecasted to break 104 degrees) became too oppressive. When we arrived on-site, we were the only visitors there. Prepared to sit this climb out with Alex, at that moment I decided I had been presented with an opportunity. There was no one around, and if he got angry and had a tantrum over the suggestion that he try a climb, we had the privacy to work through it with him. It just dawned on me that we were both going to miss out on a lot if he remained fearful. Certainly he needed to give this a try. I could accept his inability to do this more readily if I knew he had tried. So many of Alex's fears are based not on real factors so much as they are a vestige of his communication disorder and his need for sticking to safe routines. We had already made plans to attempt the New Jersey Lighthouse Challenge later that fall, and the idea of turn-taking with Joe while one son went up and one stayed at the base wasn't a good recipe for family togetherness. After five years of tag-team parenting, Joe and I were beginning to realise that for everyone's sake, we needed to do more things together as a family.

Alex's violent reaction to the suggestion was immediate.

"I AM NOT GOING UP!" The screaming was blood-curdling and as he dropped to the ground, he began kicking and pounding. This went on for several minutes. I waited for the storm to pass.

"Are you done?"

"Yes," he said and stood back up.

"There are times we do things for Alex, and there are times we do things for Ben. Ben always goes to the aquariums with you and tries the things you like. Now is a time when we do something for Ben. This is what families do."

He dropped back to the ground and began to flail around again, screaming.

Silently I thanked God for the fact that no one was around to witness the meltdown and wonder what my son's problem was. Or wonder what my problem was. This was hard enough without the judgment, but having started down the path, I knew that I couldn't let him off the hook now; to do so would reinforce the idea that a tantrum can get him out of a task he doesn't want to do. Like it or not, I now had to get him to climb. There was no going back.

"It sure is hot," I continued, as I sat down on the floor near him. "As soon as we are done climbing up, we'll go back to Grandma's and go in the pool."

I had his attention now.
"Do you want the pool?" I asked

"YES!" he said.

"Well, let's climb up and get it over with, ok? First we climb, then we swim "

"YOU ARE THE WORST MOTHER EVER!" he screamed.

"Alex, if you really, really hate this you will never have to climb up another lighthouse again. I promise. You'll never know if you don't try."

"Alright, alright!" He stood up, approached the stairs and took a step.

"Good job, Alex, I'm right behind you!"

The 191 steps to the top were, in some respects, the hardest I have ever taken with my son. I was beginning to doubt the wisdom of what I was making Alex do, wondering if I had pushed too hard, too fast. Were we going to regress and have setbacks? Did I just ruin our trip? I had no idea. As he bombarded me with a stream of verbal attacks, complete with a full listing of my inadequacies as a mother, peppered with a few "I hate you"s for good measure, I reminded myself that some mothers never hear any words from their children at all and to just be thankful he could tell me he hated me. His words and ability to express this intense anger were a gift.

As Alex stepped onto the deck of the lens chamber from the opening in the floor at the top of Old Cape Henry, I heard him draw a breath in sharply. I prepared myself for the worst.

Magic.

A slow, drawn out "Wow," emerged from my son. "This is great up here!"

"YOU SEE!" I shouted "YOU DID IT, ALEX, YOU DID IT! YOU ARE SO AWESOME!"

When we reached the bottom and made our way outside, I posed the boys in front of New Cape Henry and snapped a picture of them, both smiling, arms wrapped around each other.

I showed the picture to my son through the camera's view screen and said to him, "I am going to put this where you can see it at home, because I always want you to remember how awesome you are for overcoming your fear! There is nothing you can't do as long as you try!"

His eyes darted to mine before slipping away, his voice caught as he tried to hold back his tears. In a rare moment, he spontaneously hugged me and through the squeeze he said, "Thank you for making me do that, Mom. Thanks for making me go to the top." Three years later, Joe, Alex, Ben and I have climbed more than twenty structures across New Jersey, Virginia and North Carolina, including a week-long trek to the Outer Banks to climb Cape Hatteras, the tallest lighthouse in America. This was the first family vacation we have ever been able to take. Both of the boys handled the changes in routine and unfamiliar surroundings better than we had ever hoped. Joe and I can honestly say that we have grown to love these beacons as much as our children do. Ben has amassed an enviable collection of Scaasis lighthouses; he will be more than happy to tell you about each and every one of them whether you want to hear about them or not. His first and second grade school journals are full of lighthouse stories; most of them full of facts…

some peppered with an attempt at fiction that is much more difficult for him to generate.

Alex's journal entries about the lighthouses are different. They are much less frequent, much more simple, but far more powerful. They are not full of facts the way his writings about dinosaurs, animals, the Presidents, or natural disasters are. Instead his lighthouse story is seemingly a simple statement of a very important, breakthrough moment in his life. This is the only emotional, episodic memory that he can articulate so far; one that is always written the same way, one that is probably our biggest achievement together to date.

"My proudest moment was when I climbed the lighthouse. I got over my fear. I know I can try new things now even if they scare me at first."

George Putnam, Commissioner of Lighthouses from 1910-1935, once said, "Lighthouses are never-ceasing watchfulness; of steadfast endurance; of widespread helpfulness." I wholeheartedly agree with the sentiment. They are a helpful, hopeful symbol to me, linked to both of my sons' continuing triumphs over autism in so many ways. So much of our experience with autism has been dependent on how we choose to view the challenges it presents. What if, along the way, we had decided that Ben's lighthouses were an "obsession" or "perseveration" that we somehow needed to reduce, quell, or otherwise control? By joining Ben in his interest, we bonded as a family. Ben shared his excitement and joy with us and continues to do so. By pulling Alex out of his comfort zone and into his brother's, we have given him a powerful memory to sustain him in the frightening moments when he has to leave his comfort zone. In these beautiful, enduring structures, climbing with other enthusiasts, people who meet Alex and Ben don't see two boys with autism. They just see two boys who share their love of lighthouses. I have no idea what these people think about their mother, who can be seen watching her boys race ahead, with a smile on her face and tears in her eyes at the same time. I don't really care; I'm too busy reveling in the strides they are both making right in front of me, and how far they have surpassed my expectations in so many wonderful ways.

If I can say anything to a new mother about how to start the rollercoaster of autism, it is this: give yourself permission to occasionally forget the jargon and terminology, and instead embrace your child for who he or she is at the moment. Take the time to join your child in his world, and you may be surprised that eventually, you will find the strength and tenacity to pull your child out of their world and into yours, no matter how briefly.

And it is my steadfast and enduring hope that every mother is blessed to hear her child thank her for that.

Information about his photo essays:

5 years old (Ben) and 8 years old (Alex): Beacons of Hope was written

9 years old (Ben): his still life drawing was made

Ben

Acknowledgements

As in typical development, no single child with an Autism Spectrum Disorder (ASD) diagnosis is the same. Thanks to a combination of early diagnosis and early intervention at the Kennedy Krieger Institute (KKI) Center for Autism and Related Disorders, children with ASD have more enriched lives, filled with hope and possibility. Some continue to improve social skills, some improve to the point where they lead normal lives, some seem to grow out of the diagnosis altogether, some turn out to be gifted, and so on. All positive.

During visits and conversations with other parents of children with ASD, I noticed that some parents carefully used the phrase "had the ASD diagnosis" because they knew their children may grow out of the diagnosis or turn out to be gifted or something else. Never, never, never give up is the mindset of parents of children with ASD – signs of improvement are shining somewhere…

Children with ASD are unique or different in the eyes of parents of so-called "ordinary" children. However, I would say that the unique qualities of children with ASD have the potential to change the world. Among the children I met in making this book, I could see a future scientist, a future neurosurgeon, a future actor, a future mathematician, a future writer, a future inventor and so on. This book is dedicated to raising awareness about autism, with a special focus on autism when intellectual abilities are normal, which seems to be misunderstood widely.

Over five years passed since I initiated discussion about making a book with Dr. Landa in London. A number of parents and contributors in the Kennedy Krieger Institute (KKI) community provided us with stories to share. I truly thank them for their generosity and courage to share their precious children with the world through the images and stories.

Our journey continues but, thanks to the KKI experience, our life has been in a different chapter.

MAKIKO
January 2014

The contributors
In alphabetical order:

Christine Bakter
Jennifer and Trey Brown
Nancy Burrows – a contributing editor
Chase Johnson
Lisa Watson

Special thanks to:
Andrew Hall
Alex Majoli of Magnum Photos
Bill Procter of the bill procter creative consultancy
Dr. John T. Walkup, Professor of Psychiatry, Vice Chair, Department of Psychiatry
Director, Division of Child and Adolescent Psychiatry, Weill Cornell Medical College
and New York Presbyterian Hospital

Corporate Sponsors:
Coblentz Patch Duffy & Bass LLP
Healogix

Individual Sponsors:
Lawrence Baxter

Michael Graham

Kathleen and Joseph Hall

Kiyo Hanishi

Curt Myers

Sayoko Shirai

All proceeds go to Dr. Rebecca Landa's research on autism and developmental disorders at the Kennedy Krieger Institute's Center for Autism and Related Disorders.